Bill

A first story about living things

Written by Tim Healey
Illustrated by Sophie Harrison-Knibbs

Billy found an unusual rock when he was out walking. It was smooth and gleaming and streaked with different colours. 'What a beauty,' said his brother, Bobby.

Billy took the rock home and found a cardboard box to keep it in. He kept it in his bedroom.

He looked at it and stroked it nearly every day. It was a very nice rock.

One day they held a 'Pet's Day' at school. Julie took her kitten.

Josh took his hamster.

Laura took her rabbit.

And Billy brought his rock.
Vicky laughed and said,
'That's not a pet, Billy!'

'Oh yes, it is!' said Billy. 'It's my pet!'
'A pet is something you cuddle, silly!'
said Vicky.
'Well, I cuddle my rock,' Billy replied.

'B-b-but a pet has to have legs and fur and stuff!' Vicky complained.

'No, it doesn't!' said Alexis. 'Look at my goldfish. It's my pet, but it doesn't have those things!'

Billy smiled contentedly while his friends peered into the shoebox, looking puzzled. They all knew a rock couldn't be a pet, but they couldn't explain why.   Suddenly Josh yelled, 'I know! A rock is not a living thing. A pet must be a living thing.'

'That's it!' Laura nodded. 'Living things are different from rocks. Living things grow and need feeding. What do you feed your rock, Billy? Burgers?' All the children laughed. Billy had to think quickly.

'So, a pet has to be a living thing that grows and needs feeding, eh?' Billy grinned. 'Then I can bring a bunch of daffodils next time? They must be living things because they grow and need feeding with soil and water. I'll bring my Pet Daffodils!'

No one had an answer to that, so they
went into class and put all their pets
on a table at the back. 'What a lovely
collection of pets,' said the teacher.
'There's a little fluffy kitten and a
hoppity rabbit and a busy little mouse
on its wheel and . . .'

'. . . EEEK! WHAT'S THAT!'
'It's Billy's Pet Rock,' said Josh.
'But a rock can't be a pet, can it?'
'No,' answered the teacher.
'A pet has to be a living thing.'

'But plants are living things and they can't be pets, can they?' asked Vicky. 'No,' replied the teacher. 'But there are two types of living things - plants and animals. A pet is usually an animal.'

'You can't have a pet tree . . .

or a pet bush . . .'

'or a pet dandelion . . .

or a pet cactus.'

'But you can have a pet monkey . . .
or a pet budgerigar . . .'

'or a pet lizard . . .

or even a pet spider.'

'Plants are living things that grow and need feeding.'

'They have roots in the soil, and although they can sway in the wind, they can't move from place to place. You don't see plants taking a walk!'

'Animals are different. They can move around of their own accord. They can walk and run . . .'

'Some can hop, and some can swim.'

'Some can slither, and some can fly!'

'A rock, Billy, is not an animal or even a plant. It doesn't move around on its own. It has no roots and it doesn't grow. It doesn't eat or drink. In fact, it doesn't need feeding at all!'

Billy looked into his box and nodded.
'I have to admit,' he said, 'my rock
isn't a big eater!'

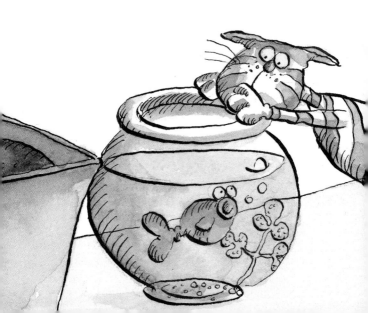

At playtime, Billy waited for his brother to come out from his class. 'My rock can't be a pet after all,' he said glumly.

When he explained why, Bobby frowned.
'So a plant can't be a pet either!' Billy
shook his head. 'Now I have nothing
to show!'

Suddenly, Bobby smiled.
'I've got an idea!' Billy listened,
then laughed.
'I can't wait to see their faces!'

After playtime, Billy went back to his classroom. 'Can I bring a pet even if it's only mine for today?' he asked the teacher.

'Of course,' answered the teacher. 'Anything that's alive, grows, needs feeding and moves by itself is fine.'

'Great!' said Billy.
'I'll just fetch him.'

'His name is Bobby!'

Everything can be divided
into things that are alive and things
that are not. Living things can be either
plants or animals.

All living things grow and change.
They need food to stay alive and healthy.
Also, animals are able to
move around by themselves.

All living things can make new ones
of their own kind. Many humans and
animals have babies; birds hatch eggs;
and plants reproduce from seeds.